Primary Specials

ANCIENT GREECE

C000220428

Mary Green

© 2004 Folens Limited, on behalf of the author

United Kingdom: Folens Publishers, Apex Business Centre, Boscombe Road, Dunstable, LU5 4RL
Email: folens@folens.com

Ireland: Folens Publishers, Greenhills Road, Tallaght, Dublin 24
Email: info@folens.ie

Poland: JUKA, ul. Renesansowa 38, Warsaw 01-905

Editor: Helen Oakes   Layout artist: Patricia Hollingsworth

Illustrations: Catherine Ward   Cover design: Martin Cross

Cover image by permission of Mary Evans Picture Library

First published 2004 by Folens Limited.

British Library Cataloguing in Publication Data. A catalogue record for this publication is available from the British Library.

ISBN 1 84303 064 0

Contents

We hope you enjoy using this new *Primary Specials!* book, to be used with children achieving at a lower level. The book has been written in response to market research with teachers. The focus is a central resource that is entirely visual, with a few exceptions that are written resources, such as historical stories. Accompanying this are support materials. The book follows the revised National Curriculum for History (History 2000) and the QCA scheme of work at Key Stage 2.

New *Primary Specials!* contain 15 separate chapters, each covering a new topic within the theme of the book. The resource and activity pages are photocopiable and are accompanied by a page of notes for the teacher. This page is laid out as follows:

Background
– gives useful information on the topic, which the teacher can draw on as needed.

Working with the resource
– gives guidance on using the resource as the focus of group discussion, which should be led by the teacher or a support assistant. **Useful questions** are also included.

Using the activity sheets
– provides information on the differentiated tasks related to the resource. The activity pages often include graphic organisers such as spidergrams, writing frames and chronological and other models, to support pupils' thinking and recording.

Skills
Important historical skills are included across the books. These should be within the children's abilities, such as:
– promoting the sense of the passage of time
– sequencing events and promoting a sense of chronology
– distinguishing between simple fact and opinion
– recognising that while some things change others stay the same
– promoting empathy through identifying with lives in the past
– recognising simple cause and effect.

Why not look for these other titles in the series?

Ancient Egypt	FC0616
Children in the Second World War	FC0608
Children in Victorian Britain	FC0624
Invaders and Settlers in Britain	FC0586
Tudor Times	FC0594
How Life Has Changed Since 1948	FC0632

Can't find the topic you are looking for? If you have any ideas for other titles to be covered in the *Primary Specials!* series write and let us know:

Publishing Department
Folens Publishers
Unit 20
Apex Business Centre
Boscombe Road
Dunstable
Beds LU5 4RL

Greece

Background

Greek communities grew out of isolated tribes that settled in the rough, hilly terrain. From these developed numerous city-states such as Athens, Sparta and Corinth. They all had their own way of life and were often suspicious of each other, making enemies or forming tactical alliances. But they would all come together as Grecians to repel outside enemies. The Greek age reached its height in the fifth century BC, after which it was weakened by war and invasion until eventually it became part of the Roman Empire.

Summers were hot and winters cool. Farming was precarious. However, grapes, olives, figs, beans, cucumbers, other vegetables and flax were grown along with barley and wheat, which were also imported. Sheep and goats provided milk, leather or wool. Poultry, eggs and wild birds were also eaten. Fish was a luxury.

Using the activity sheet

'Brainstorming'

The children could work in pairs to build up a picture of Greece and record additional words such as: sun, hills, goats, olives, boat, islands, Athens, Sparta and so on.

Working with the resources

'What does the picture tell you?'

Talk about the climate and landscape of Greece and the isolation of early communities. Note that although modern Greece is very different from Ancient Greece, the climate and landscape is much the same. Children who have connections with the country could make special contributions.

'Where is Greece?'

The first map should give the children an idea of the distance between Greece and Britain. The second map shows the Ancient Greek world. Explain that this refers to the distant past (you could introduce the term BC if suitable) and discuss the isolation of the Greek islands.

Useful questions

'What does the picture tell you?'

1 Do you think it is a hot or cold country? Why?
2 What are the trees and plants like?
3 What animals are there?
4 What do you think farming was like?
5 How easy do you think it would be to travel around?

'Where is Greece?'

1 Find Greece on map 1.
2 Find Britain.
3 Is Greece near or faraway?
4 Look at map 2. How do you think the Ancient Greeks travelled to the islands?
5 How do people travel today? (Still mainly by boat.)

What does the picture tell you?

PRIMARY SPECIALS! *Ancient Greece*

Where is Greece?

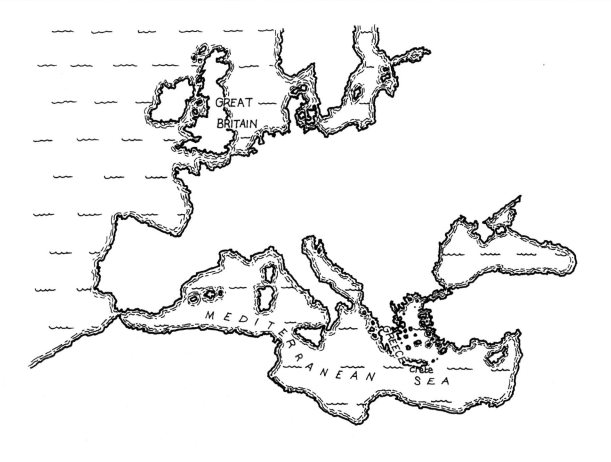

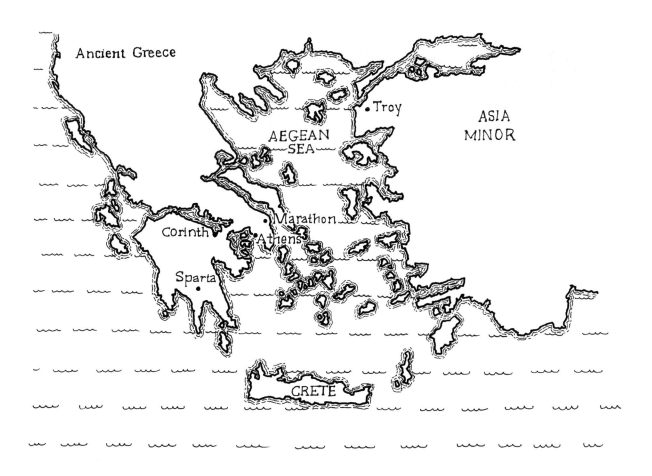

Brainstorming

What can you remember about Ancient Greece?

Think about:

- the picture you have seen
- the maps you have looked at
- anything else you know.

List at least ten things. The first three have been done for you.

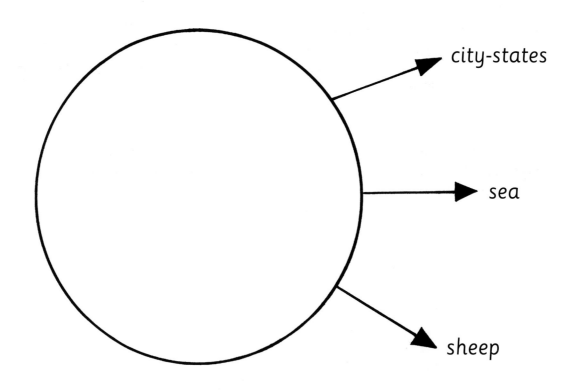

Domestic Buildings

Background

The Greek house was the woman's province. It was made of mud bricks and usually had a tiled roof and a few small windows with wooden shutters. Wealthy families might have bathrooms but there were no toilets. Some also had additional rooms for guests. Oil lamps made of clay were used at night. Most houses were built around a courtyard and had one or two storeys. The cooking area would be in or near the courtyard, which often had a well. There was usually a main room or hall and the women had their own rooms away from male society. These were sometimes above the verandah (called an exedra), which looked out on to the courtyard. In summer the household might sit out on the verandah or in the courtyard.

Although Greek women had little power in the external world, they would have exercised some at home, simply because they were confined there and were responsible for organising the household, including the slaves who did most of the domestic chores. Poorer women took on a range of jobs – in the market, selling goods or in the fields picking fruit – and would work alongside men.

Working with the resource

'The Greek house'

Discuss the main features of the house with the children so that they can complete the activity sheet, 'The house plan'. You can refer to the key on the activity sheet for guidance. You may wish to go through the key with the children, for example discussing whereabouts in the illustration the staircase would be, as it cannot be seen. (It would be internal. See plan.)

Useful questions

1 Where do you think the courtyard was? Why do you think there was a courtyard?
2 Can you find the verandah?
3 Where did people get their water from?
4 Where do you think they cooked?
5 Most houses did not have bathrooms. This one has. Why do you think that is?
6 How would you get up to the second storey?
7 What do you think the house is built from?
8 How is the house different from yours?

Using the activity sheets

'The house plan'

The children will need the resource to match the plan of the house to the illustration. Once they are sure where everything is, they can number the plan.

'Fact or opinion?'

Here the children are asked to distinguish between fact and opinion and also to provide facts of their own. They should draw on previous discussions. Facts might focus on the roof, hall, bathroom, cooking area and climate.

The Greek house

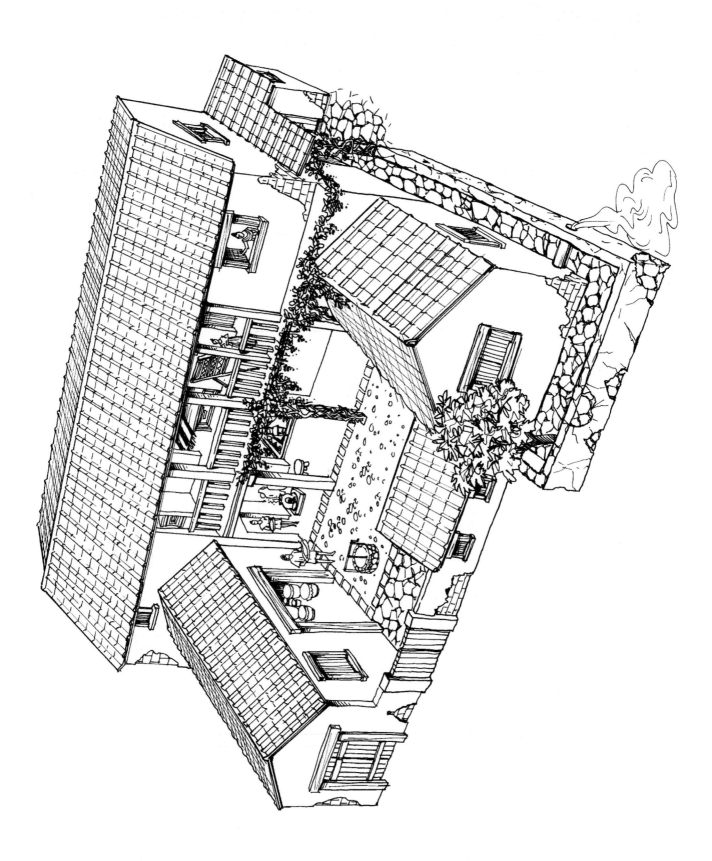

The house plan

You will need the picture, 'The Greek house'.
Find the places listed in the key. Then number each place correctly on the plan. Some have been done for you.

Key		
1 hall or main room	**4** women's rooms	**7** cooking area
2 courtyard	**5** staircase	**8** well
3 upper verandah	**6** bathroom	**9** store rooms

Ground floor

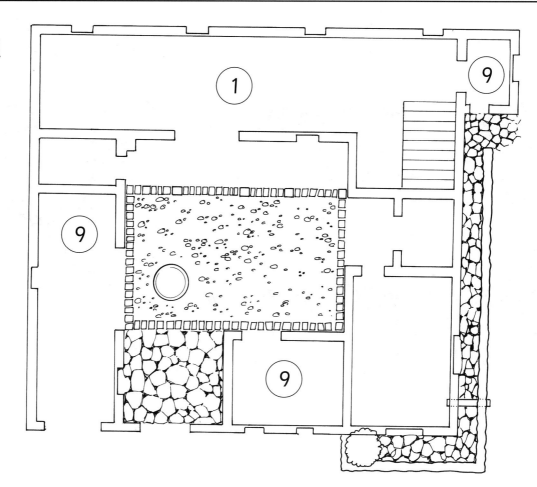

Upper floor

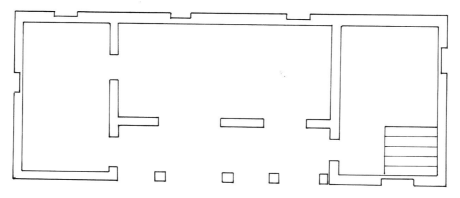

Fact or opinion?

Read the sentences about the Greek house. They are either a fact (true) or an opinion (someone's point of view).

Tick the correct box for each sentence.

	Fact	**Opinion**
Most houses were made of mud brick.	☐	☐
The house was built around a courtyard.	☐	☐
It must have been pleasant to sit out in summer.	☐	☐
There was often a well in the courtyard.	☐	☐
Men should have helped in the home.	☐	☐
Women were not allowed to go out much.	☐	☐
The windows were too small.	☐	☐
The women had their own rooms.	☐	☐

Write down two facts of your own about the Greek house.

_____

_____

Clothes, Textiles and Jewellery

Background

Clothes were made from wool and flax and occasionally silk, and they were very simple. They were essentially a rectangular piece of cloth that could be worn in various ways. The most common garment was a chiton and was worn by men and women. The cloth was folded in half and the two sides sewn together. The open part at the top was pinned together leaving a space for the head to go through. Once it had been put on, it draped down over the shoulders forming a type of sleeve on either side. A belt was added and the material either pulled up or left according to how long you wished the skirt to be. Fabric could be dyed and patterns were often added around the edge. Saffron, for example, was used to create a vivid yellow.

In winter, when it was cooler, a cloak was added called a himation, and in summer when the sun was fierce, the man wore a wide-brimmed hat called a petasos that was tied under the chin. Shoes were leather sandals, although the poor usually went without. The wealthy had jewellery made from hammered gold and silver, and designs could be intricate. Men wore rings and women wore necklaces, bracelets, anklets and earrings. Most Greeks, if they could afford it, wore brooches or pins to secure their clothes.

Working with the resource

'Greek fashion'

The illustration shows a Greek woman wearing a patterned chiton, with her hair tied back in a fashionable style. She also wears a belt, delicate gold earrings and brooches at her shoulders. Use as much of the background information as you can to discuss the picture with the children.

Useful questions

1 Describe what the woman is wearing.
2 How is her dress secured?
3 What is the pattern like?
4 Do you know the name for her type of dress?
5 What kind of jewellery is she wearing?
6 Do you think she is rich or poor? How can you tell?

Using the activity sheets

'What is she wearing?'

The children are asked to identify the main points about the woman's dress and her jewellery. Encourage them to use appropriate vocabulary, such as 'chiton'.

'Greek designs'

The children are asked to create a design that would suit a chiton. There are several patterns in the frame of the activity sheet that they could refer to. The writing frame should help them to write a brief caption about their designs but they could always add more.

Greek fashion

What is she wearing?

Answer the questions in the boxes.

What clothing is she wearing?

What is it made of?

How is it held together?

Where are the patterns?

What is she wearing on her feet?

What are they made of?

Describe her hair.

What jewellery is she wearing?

What is it made of?

Greek designs

Work out a Greek design for the cloth below.
You could design a border for the edge or a pattern for the centre.
Try out lots of designs in rough first before drawing in the box below.
When you have drawn your design, finish the caption at the bottom of the page.

The design above has different shapes in it such as

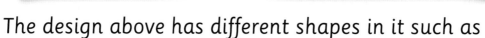

_____

The material the cloth is made of is

_____

The cloth will be made into

_____

PRIMARY SPECIALS! *Ancient Greece*

Athenians

This unit can be used with the next one to compare life in Athens and Sparta.

Background

Athens was the most important city-state in Greece. It was cultured and highly developed. Philosophy, politics, government, the arts and sciences flourished and Athenian culture has had a lasting effect. Boys began school at the age of six or seven. They were taught to read and write, to sing and to play an instrument such as the lyre. Physical education was important and was taught at the gymnasium, which was also a meeting place. Some boys went on to study further subjects such as mathematics and drama.

Girls received no formal education, although some from wealthy families became literate and a few, such as the poet Sappho, became well-known. Most unmarried daughters were taught skills such as sewing and spinning (hence the name 'spinster'). Married women did weaving. However, as Greece was a slave culture, women did few domestic chores. House slaves might also work in the fields. Others would take care of the children and even teach them.

Working with the resource

'A scene from Athens'

You can use the illustration to explain to the children what life in Athens would have been like. Note in particular the architecture, the different activities that the boys and girls are doing and the work of the slaves. It would be useful to introduce words such as 'lyre', 'loom', 'weaving', 'spinning' and 'flax', if these have not been discussed already.

Useful questions

1 What are the boys doing? (Having lessons)
2 What are the girls doing? (Helping at home)
3 Who else is doing the chores? (Slaves)
4 Can you find the speaker and crowd? What do you think is happening? (You might like to discuss Speakers' Corner at Hyde Park in London, to explain the point.)
5 Can you find the olive grove? What are the slaves doing?

Using the activity sheets

'Life in Athens'

The children can answer these simple questions after the discussion. The activity should help them to understand the differentiated nature of Greek society.

'Nika'

This activity sheet can be used with 'Milon' in the next unit to compare the life of an Athenian child with a Spartan one. To complete the sentences the words should be written in this order: flax, spin, read, tablet, lessons, boys, basket, figs. (Please note that the task is written on a 'clay tablet'.)

A scene from Athens

Life in Athens

Look at the picture 'A scene from Athens'.
Match each question to the correct answer by drawing a line.
Sometimes you will need to draw more than one line to the same answer.
The first has been done for you.

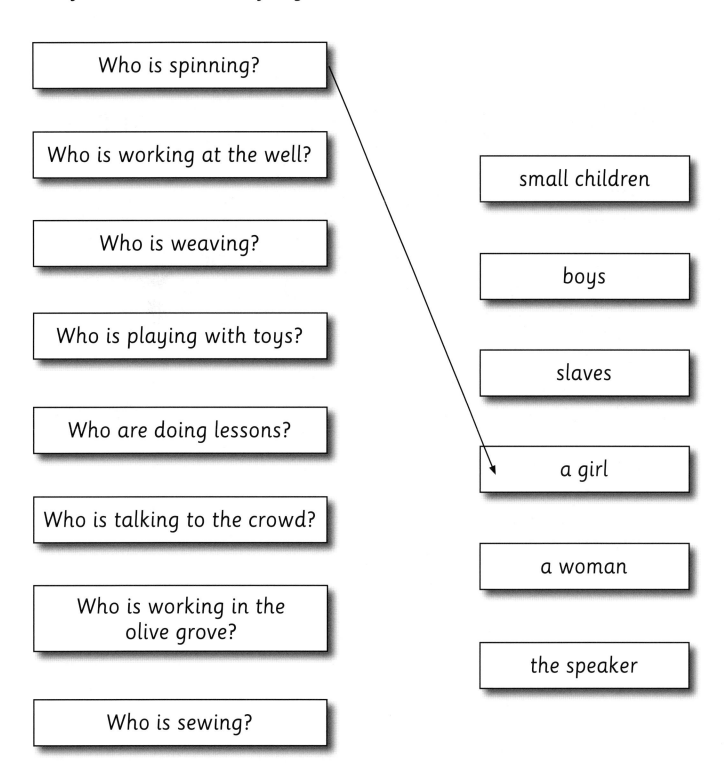

Who is spinning?	small children
Who is working at the well?	boys
Who is weaving?	slaves
Who is playing with toys?	a girl
Who are doing lessons?	a woman
Who is talking to the crowd?	the speaker
Who is working in the olive grove?	
Who is sewing?	

PRIMARY SPECIALS! *Ancient Greece*

Nika

Nika lives in Athens. She is writing about her day.

Read all the sentences first.
Then finish each one by choosing the best word
from the box below.

Today mother showed me some cloth made of

Because she is teaching me how to

She has already taught me to

And, as you can see, to write on a clay

I am lucky. My friend Polla will not do

Her mother says reading and writing is only for

In the afternoon our slave brought fruit from the fields in her

The fruit I like best is

Words

figs   **read**   **flax**   **boys**   **tablet**   **spin**   **lessons**   **basket**

PRIMARY SPECIALS! *Ancient Greece*

Spartans

This unit can be used with the previous one to compare life in Athens and Sparta.

Background

Our information about Sparta, which was situated in the Peloponnese, largely comes from Athenian records and since Athens and Sparta were enemies, these records may not be reliable. However, it would appear that the Spartans were almost entirely concerned with military perfection. Boys began learning how to fight and survive by themselves from an early age. They were given little food and encouraged to find their own, in an effort to produce soldiers who could endure difficult conditions. Even when first married they lived in military barracks. Girls were trained to be hardy too. How far they followed the same pursuits as boys is not clear, but they were physically fit. They were also literate, as were the boys. In this respect, Spartan girls differed from most Athenian girls. Spartan women also had greater freedom, partly because the men were away fighting. Generally however, life appears to have been brutal for all Spartans. Weak babies were left to die, for example.

Working with the resource

'A scene from Sparta'

Use the illustration to explain to the children what life would have been like in Sparta in contrast to life in Athens. Point out that we use the word 'spartan' to mean 'basic conditions, without luxury'.

Useful questions

1 What is the weather like? (Windy and cool – NB the Athenians would have worn warmer clothes.)
2 What are the boys and girls doing?
3 What are their clothes like? What have they got on their feet?
4 How are the children being treated?
5 What are the buildings like compared to those in Athens?

Using the activity sheets

'What were the Spartans like?'

Most children should be able to read the words by themselves, but they could work in pairs if necessary. They should circle the following: hard, strong, brave, mean, cruel, firm, fierce, tough.

'Milon'

Use this activity sheet with 'Nika' in the previous unit. When the children have completed both, they can take it in turns to read them to each other and discuss the differences. The answers are as follows: hungry, eat, bread, caught, fight, soldier, battles, Sparta.

A scene from Sparta

PRIMARY SPECIALS! *Ancient Greece*

What were the Spartans like?

Draw a circle around all the adjectives that tell you what the
Spartans were like.

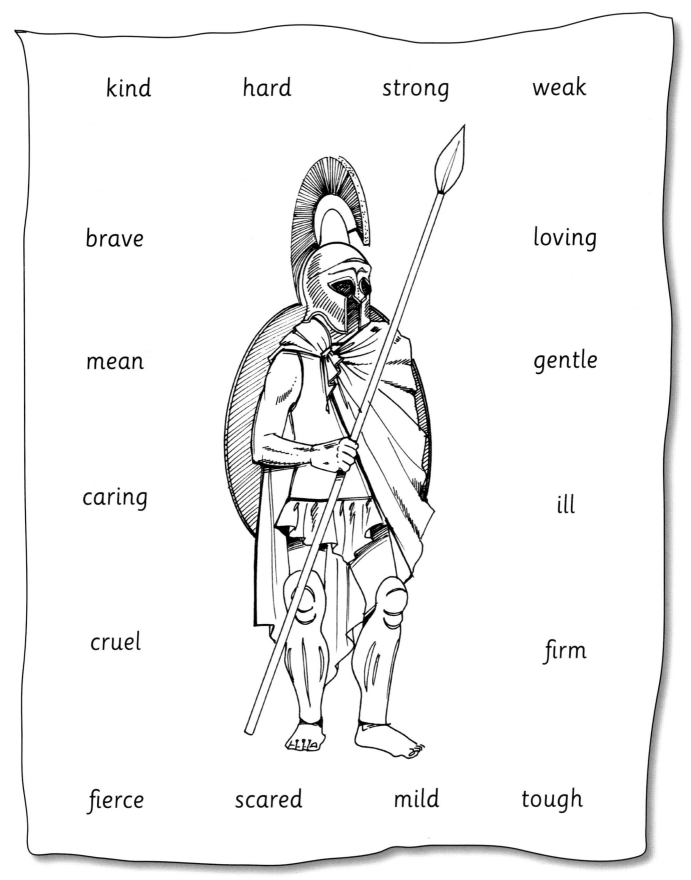

kind   hard   strong   weak

brave   loving

mean   gentle

caring   ill

cruel   firm

fierce   scared   mild   tough

Milon

Milon is a Spartan boy. He is writing about his day at school.

Read all the sentences first.
Then finish each one by choosing the best word from the box below.

This morning when I woke up I was

Because we are given very little to

But I was able to steal some

Without being

I am learning how to wrestle and how to

I will become a strong

And fight in many

And I will always be loyal to

Words

fight   **bread**   **caught**   **soldier**   **Sparta**

hungry   **eat**   **battles**

PRIMARY SPECIALS! *Ancient Greece*   © Folens (copiable page)

Warfare

Background

The trireme was the Greek's main warship. It was a narrow wooden galley that was built low off the ground. It was mobile and swift, making it ideal for engagements near the coast, where most of the battles took place. It was powered by oars and the rowers were arranged in three rows ('trireme' means 'three oars'). Citizens from the poorer sections of society were used as rowers. Also on board there were archers, spearsmen, sailors, a carpenter and the 'proreus', who was the look-out. Captains were usually powerful Greeks, but in practice the helmsmen ran the ships. Since triremes could sail close to each other, battering rams were used to cause extensive damage.

The Greek soldier or 'hoplite' carried a spear, sword and shield. His bronze armour consisted of a breastplate and backplate, and a helmet. He also wore 'greaves', which protected the legs and ankles. When a soldier left for war his family performed a ritual. The family shared wine together as a gesture of unity and some was also poured on the ground as an offering.

Working with the resource

'Armour and warships'

You might like to take the children through these illustrations while referring to unfamiliar vocabulary such as 'armour', 'trireme', 'hoplite' and 'greaves' at the same time. They can then be encouraged to use these terms in the discussion. You might also like to mention the family ritual conducted for soldiers before they went to war and the trireme's effectiveness in coastal battles.

Useful questions

1 Describe what the soldier is wearing. Why is he wearing it?
2 Do you know the words for the different parts of his armour?
3 Look at the ship. From what do you think it is made?
4 What makes it move? (Mainly the oars, although the sail might have been used when the ship was not in combat.)
5 The trireme could move quickly. Can you work out why?

Using the activity sheets

'Words and their meanings'

The children should match the items listed to their uses. The task will help to reinforce the meaning of new vocabulary, some of which they could try to use in the next activity sheet.

'Soldier or sailor?'

Here the children can imagine what it might be like to be a Greek soldier or sailor. Encourage them to ask questions relevant to military life or to any other information discussed earlier.

Armour and warships

Words and their meanings

What do these words mean? Can you remember?
Draw a line to match the names to their meanings.
The first has been done for you.

Names

Meanings

hoplite

armour

greaves

breastplate

backplate

helmsman

trireme

battle dress

metal to protect the chest in battle

metal to protect the back in battle

a warship

a foot soldier

a sailor who took charge of steering the ship

metal to protect the legs and ankles in battle

Soldier or sailor?

If you could meet an Ancient Greek soldier or sailor what questions would you ask?
Here is an example question for a soldier:

1 *What did you say to your family when you left for war?*

And here is one for a sailor:

1 *What is your job on the trireme?*

Choose either a soldier or a sailor and write down the questions you would ask.

2 Where _____

_____

3 What _____

_____

4 How _____

_____

5 Which _____

_____

6 Can _____

_____

7 Are _____

_____

Some useful words

battle   injury   wife   children   Athens   Sparta   oars

helmsman   spear   shield

Marathon

Background

Persia began to invade Greece around 500–490 BC. The Persians were an important power with a large empire. The Persian wars, as they became known, involved several invasions, some of which the Greeks successfully repulsed. The normally separate and even hostile city-states co-operated to defend Greece, so that Athenians and Spartans, for example, came together. The Persian threat was finally eliminated in 479 BC at the Battle of Plataea. However, the Battle of Marathon was the Greek's most notable success. Their leader, Miltiades, led his small army to victory against all the odds. To what extent the messenger's achievement is true is uncertain but once the battle had been won, the Greeks repulsed another Persian fleet, based further along the coast and ready to move into Athens.

Using the activity sheets

'The battlefield'

Providing the children have understood and remembered how the Greeks outwitted the Persian army, they can do without the resource. The children need to add arrows showing:

- the Persian army advancing in the middle to attack the Greeks
- the Greeks advancing from the outsides (wings) to attack the Persians.

'Searching for the answers'

Here the children will need to have the resource available to them. Some questions give grammatical cues (for example exact structures from the passage are quoted such as 'we remember the messenger') but this is not always the case, so the children will need to understand all the events and information. The correct paragraphs are in order: 2, 2, 6, 5, 6, 3, 4, 5.

Working with the resource

'The Battle of Marathon'

You can read the resource with the children, although some may be able to read it on their own or in pairs. It outlines the main events before, during and after the battle and prompts the children to make the connection between 'Marathon' the place, the Greek messenger's achievement and the modern race. This might be an opportunity to discuss the term 'BC' and explain when the Battle of Marathon took place.

Useful questions

1 Where was Marathon?
2 Why is it famous?
3 What did the Persians want to do?
4 What problem did the Greeks have?
5 What trick did the Greeks work out to help themselves?
6 Who won the battle?
7 What did the messenger do?
8 What happened to him?
9 How is Marathon remembered today?

The Battle of Marathon

Marathon was a place in Ancient Greece. One of the most well-known battles between the Greeks and Persians was fought there.

In 490 BC the Persians landed their fleet of ships on the coast. It was not far from Marathon and from there they planned to capture Athens.

As soon as the Greeks found out they sent an army to hold back their enemy. When they got there they saw that the Persian army was huge, much bigger than the Greek army. So what could they do?

They thought of a clever trick. The Greek soldiers spread out in a line across the Marathon valley. There were not many men in the middle of the line. But they made sure that there were extra men at the two ends (the wings).

The Persians marched towards the middle. Of course they broke through the line. Then the Greek soldiers at the wings swept around and attacked. Many Persians died. The others returned to their ships.

It was said that a messenger was sent to Athens to report the Greek victory. He ran all the way – about 32 kilometres. He gave them the news but he was so tired that he collapsed and died. Today we remember the messenger each year. Can you guess how?

The battlefield

Look at the map. Tick the boxes if you can answer these questions.

Can you see where the Greek army was?

Can you see where the Persian army was?

Can you see the Persian ships in the bay?

Can you see where the messenger went?

Now draw arrows on the map to show:

● how the Persians attacked the Greeks
● how the Greeks attacked the Persians.

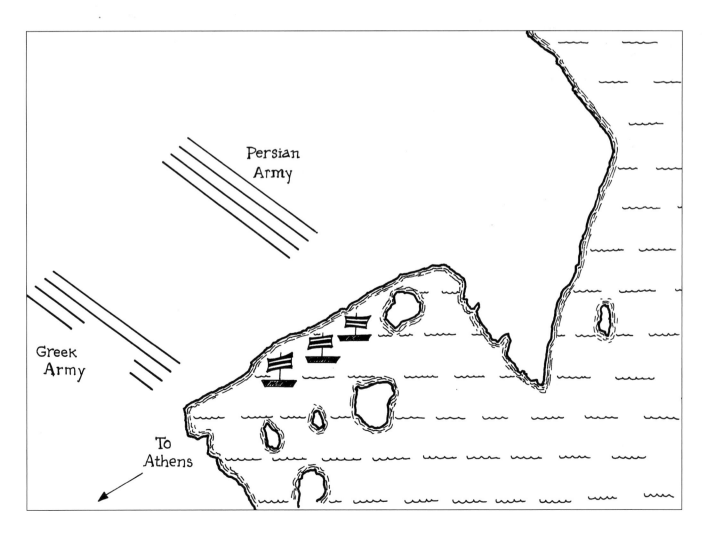

PRIMARY SPECIALS! *Ancient Greece*

Searching for the answers

The 'Battle of Marathon' has six paragraphs.
At the end of each question, write down which paragraph gives you the answer. The first one has been done for you.

Which paragraph tells you:

what the Persians planned to do? `2`

when the Battle of Marathon was? ☐

what happened to the messenger? ☐

how the Persians attacked the Greeks? ☐

how we remember the messenger today? ☐

that the Persian army was huge? ☐

how the Greeks arranged their soldiers? ☐

how the Greeks attacked the Persians? ☐

PRIMARY SPECIALS! *Ancient Greece*

Religion

Background

Religion in the Ancient Greek world was closely tied to myth. Stories of the gods and goddesses were told in all the city-states and most festivals were related to particular deities. There was no religious code or set of moral beliefs, only a sense that the gods ruled the lives of humans and that it was as well to appease them and offer sacrifices. Many deities were related to natural phenomena such as the seasons, or thunder and lightning.

The principal god was Zeus who ruled on Mount Olympus, where other important deities also lived. His brothers, Poseidon and Hades, ruled the oceans and the underworld respectively. Zeus' sister and wife was Hera but he fathered many children by different goddesses and also mortal women. There were numerous other smaller gods of the woods, mountains and lakes. Pan, the son of Hermes, was the shepherd's god. There were also demi-gods such as Perseus and Hercules who performed heroic acts, and were human-like in their nature. Heroes like these were greatly admired by the Greeks.

Using the activity sheet

'Gods and goddesses'

This activity sheet can be used as a template for recording information about a range of gods.

Working with the resources

'Zeus'

Zeus is shown with his thunderbolt. Athena rises out of the top of his head, carrying her shield. Zeus was Athena's father. Her mother, Metis, was a mortal. It was said that her son would challenge the gods before Athena was born. So Zeus swallowed Metis whole. Some time later he developed a severe pain in his head. So Hephaistos, the god of blacksmiths, split open Zeus' head with his axe and Athena was born.

'Athena'

Athena was a warrior goddess and the goddess of wisdom (as represented by the owl). She was also the Goddess of Athens. The Parthenon housed a gigantic gold statue of Athena.

Useful questions

'Zeus'

1 There are two gods and a goddess in this picture. Can you find them?
2 Which god do you think is Zeus?
3 What is the other god carrying?
4 Can you guess what has happened?
5 What has Zeus got in his right hand? (A thunderbolt.)

'Athena'

1 What kind of goddess do you think Athena is? How can you tell?
2 What is she carrying?
3 What is she wearing?
4 Do you know who her father is?
5 What is her special bird? What do you think it might represent?
6 Athena was the goddess of a city-state. Can you guess which one?

Zeus

PRIMARY SPECIALS! *Ancient Greece*   © Folens (copiable page)

Athena

Gods and goddesses

Write the name of the god or goddess in the middle. If you wish, draw a picture of him or her too.
Then complete the boxes.

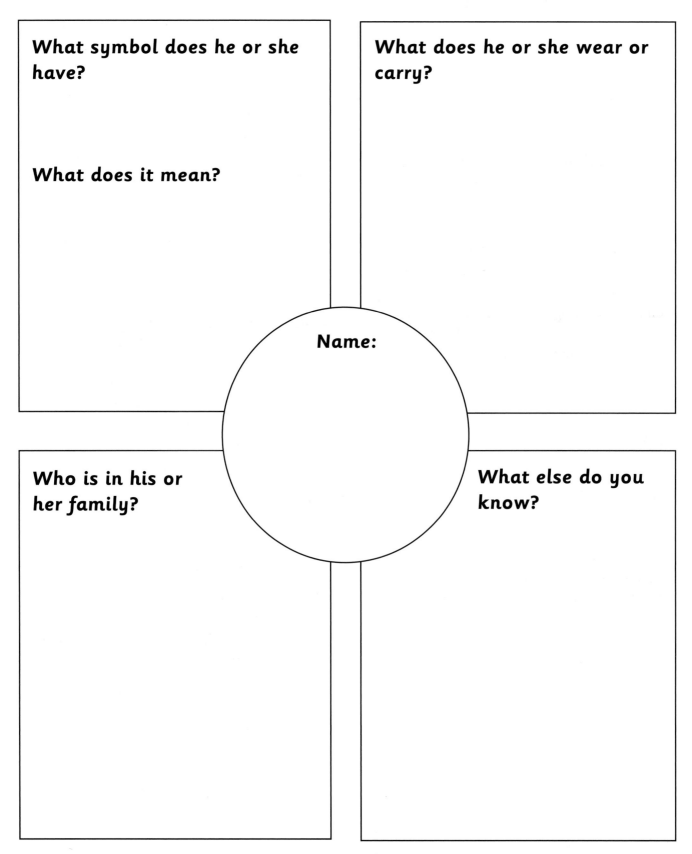

What symbol does he or she have?

What does it mean?

What does he or she wear or carry?

Name:

Who is in his or her family?

What else do you know?

PRIMARY SPECIALS! *Ancient Greece* © Folens (copiable page)

Greek Myths: The Trojan Horse

Background

The myth of the Trojan horse is one of the best known. Briefly, the story is as follows:

The Greeks and the Trojans have been at war for ten years and Odysseus devises a plan for bringing it to a close. A large wooden horse is built, which is able to secrete a party of Greek soldiers so that they can gain entry to Troy. The key to the plan's success rests on the Trojan's belief that the horse left outside the walls is a gift to the goddess Athena, to appease her and give the Greeks a fair wind to sail home. They assume, therefore, that the enemy has gone, but might return if the horse remains where it is. Cassandra, whose warnings of doom are destined forever to fall on deaf ears, is ignored. The wooden horse is taken in, the Greek soldiers creep out at night, alert their army and disaster follows for Troy.

Using the activity sheet

'Questions and answers'

Once the children have heard the story they can answer the first set of questions. They are then asked to set their own questions and give them to a partner to answer. Questions might be: What happened to it? Who was inside it? Why did the Trojans let it in?

Working with the resources

'The wooden horse pictures 1 and 2'

Tell the story of the Trojan horse to the children, emphasising in particular why the Trojans let it enter the city. You could also discuss the meaning of the expression 'a Trojan horse' as trickery or deceit. The two resources are contrasting pictures of the horse and are useful for pointing out how representations of the same feature or event can differ. The first is based on a modern representation built at Hissarlik in Turkey, where Troy once stood. The second is based on an early relief found on a jar around 650-600 BC at Mykonos.

Useful questions

'The wooden horse picture 1'

1 Look at the picture. What is it?
2 From what is it made?
3 Where would the soldiers hide?
4 How would they get there?
5 How would they look out?
6 Do you think it was made a long time ago or recently?

'The wooden horse picture 2'

1 Look at the picture. How is it different from the other one?
2 How do you think the Trojans got the horse into the city?
3 Where are the soldiers in the picture?
4 What are they wearing? What are they carrying?

The wooden horse picture 1

The wooden horse picture 2

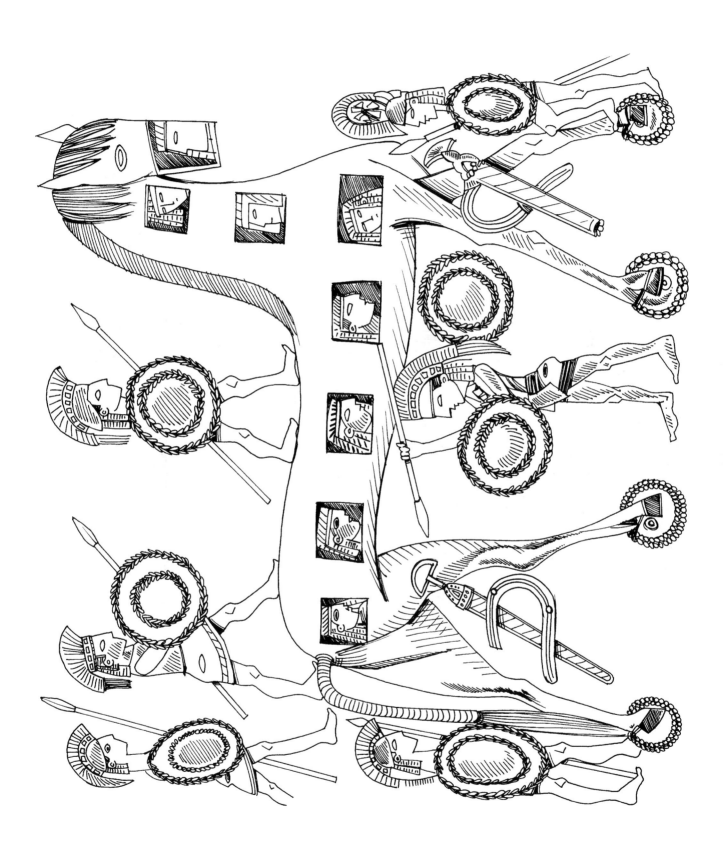

Questions and answers

1 Answer the questions in the spidergram about the wooden horse.
2 What else could you ask? Finish the other questions.
3 Give them to a partner to answer.

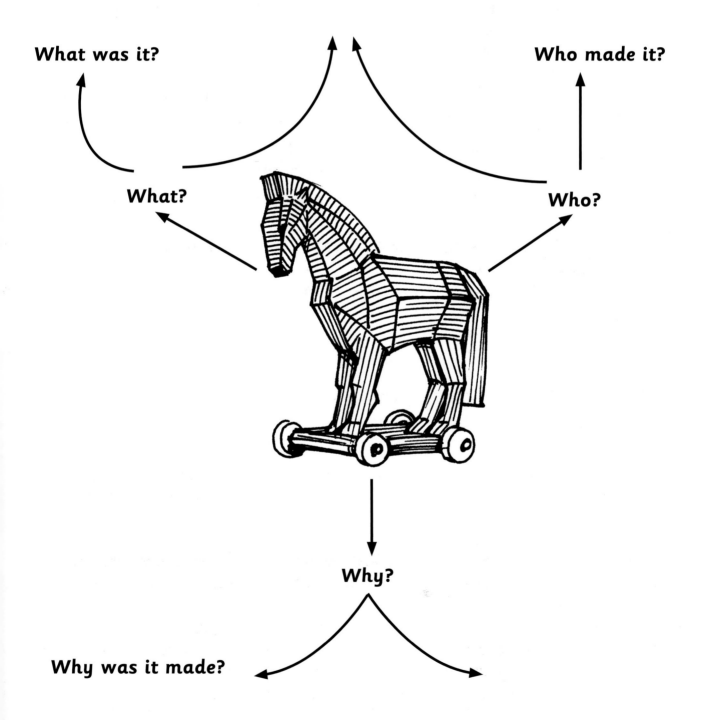

What was it?

What?

Who made it?

Who?

Why?

Why was it made?

Writing and the Alphabet

Background

The Ancient Greeks wrote in capital letters without spaces between words, so to the untrained eye it is difficult to read. There were few writing conventions or punctuation. Early writing swept from side to side in zig-zag fashion, beginning on the right and proceeding back again from the left. Later it moved from left to right for each line. Clay tablets were used to write on and then lengths of papyrus attached to a scroll. Boards covered in wax were marked with a stylus and could be re-waxed and re-used. Reed pens and ink made from vegetable matter were also used. Public declarations were often written on stone tablets.

English uses a large number of the same characters from the Ancient Greek alphabet but some represent different sounds, ('P/p' in Greek for example sounds 'r' in English). Dialects varied across Greece and of course the language changed over time.

Working with the resource

'The Greek alphabet'

Only the capitals, lower case and sounds (which varied with dialect) are given here and not the Greek names. You may wish to introduce them if applicable. They are as follows: alpha, beta, gamma, delra, epsilon, zeta, eta, theta, iota, kappa, lambda, mu, nu, xi, omicron, pi, rho, sigma, upsilon, phi, chi, psi, omega.

Useful questions

1 Which letters can you see that look the same as letters in English?
2 Are they always the same letters? Look for examples of those that are and those that aren't.
3 Can you say the sounds of the Greek alphabet?

Using the activity sheets

'Name game'

The names given are mainly three-letter words and most are made up of simple phonemes. Where they are more complex, they still have single sounds in the Greek alphabet (such as 'ph'). The names read: Tom, Max, Chen, Phil, Ruth, Pip, Sue, Anna.

'Our Greek words'

If you prefer the children could work in pairs. Some words may come to them without the aid of a dictionary but the spellings will be difficult, so it is useful to have a dictionary to hand. It is best if they find words they know, such as: alphabet, autobiography, dinosaur, hippopotamus, microchip, photograph, tricycle. Contained in these words are also the following derivations: 'bet' from beta meaning 'B'; 'bio' – bios/human life; 'graph' – graphe/writing; 'saur'- sauros/lizard; 'potamus' – potamos/river; cycle/kuklos/circle. As a further teaching point you might like to discuss that we are constantly inventing new words from old. A good example is 'microchip'. (The children should not, of course, assume that the microchip existed in Ancient Greece.)

The Greek alphabet

Capitals	Small letters	Sounds
A	α	a (like 'a' in 'cat')
B	β	b
Γ	γ	g
Δ	δ	d
E	ε	e (like 'e' in 'pet')
Z	ς	z
H	η	ay or e
Θ	θ	th
I	ι	i
K	κ	k
Λ	λ	l
M	μ	m
N	ν	n
Ξ	ξ	x or ks
O	ο	o (like 'o' in 'on')
Π	π	p
P	ρ	r
Σ	σς	s
T	τ	t
Y	υ	y or u
Φ	φ	ph or f
X	χ	ch
Ψ	ψ	ps
Ω	ω	oh

Name game

Here are some names written in Ancient Greek. Can you work them out? Write them underneath.

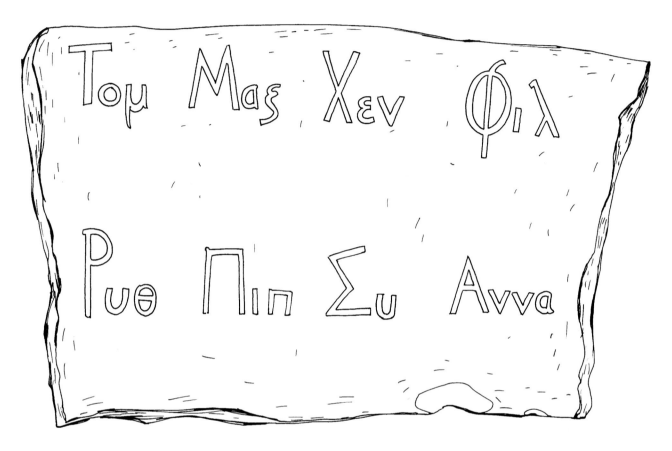

Now try writing your own name.
Are all the letters in the Greek alphabet or not?
Does your name look the same in English?

Our Greek words

We have lots of Greek words in English. They are often at the start of long words and are called prefixes.

Find English words that you know with these prefixes at the start of them. Then write them down. Use a dictionary to help you.

The first has been done for you.

Prefix	Meaning	Word
aero	air	*aeroplane*
alpha	'A'	
auto	self	
dino	terrible	
hippo	horse	
micro	small	
photo	light	
tri	three	

PRIMARY SPECIALS! *Ancient Greece*

Greek Drama

Background

Greek drama probably grew out of performances by a chorus of dancers who also sang at religious festivals for Dionysus, the god of the vine. From this developed the idea of character and the dramatic story. Performances included 'tragedy', that retold stories of the gods and later also 'comedy', that was based on everyday life. A range of emotions or 'passions' were acted out with the use of masks made from stiffened linen. Padded costumes were also worn. Like the masks, these costumes were exaggerated in style, perhaps because in the large audience many would be sitting at some distance from the stage.

Using the activity sheet

'My mask'

The outline of the mask can be adapted to suit a range of characters. For example, the hair can be extended and flowers added, although the children should remember that they will need to cut round the mask, so their designs should not be too intricate. If you prefer, the children can use the mask outline as a template to cut out a stronger mask from card. As far as possible, the children should create an authentic design and should try to show a particular emotion. They can refer to the resource, 'Greek masks' for guidance.

Working with the resources

'The theatre'

The theatre was open air. Behind the stage there was a wooden building or a painted board that was an early form of scenery. It could also act as a retiring room for the actors. The orchestra where the chorus performed was a circular structure in front of the stage. The audience sat on stone seats, which were raked and formed a large semicircle.

'Greek masks'

The human masks depicted here show the emotions: laughter, fear, anger and sadness.

Useful questions

'The theatre'

1 What kind of seats does the audience sit on?
2 What are the main parts of the theatre?
3 What is the scenery like?
4 Where do you think the actors enter?
5 Most of our theatres are indoors. Why do you think this is?

'Greek masks'

1 Choose one mask and describe it.
2 What expression does each mask have? Why?
3 Can you guess what the masks might be made of?

The theatre

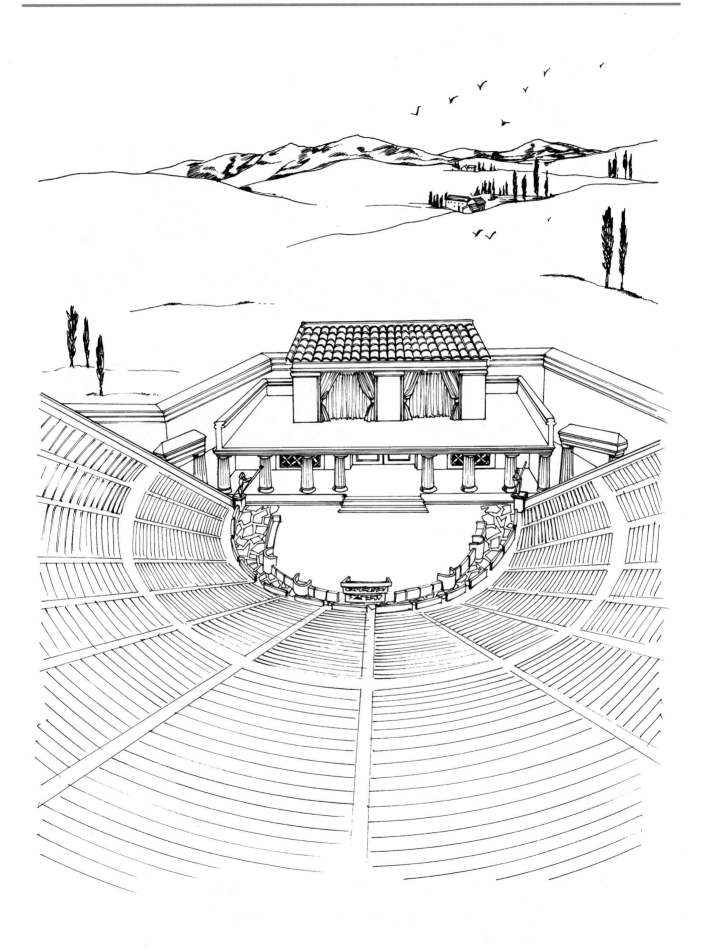

PRIMARY SPECIALS! *Ancient Greece* © Folens (copiable page)

Greek masks

My mask

You will need: scissors, string, a pencil, coloured pens or pencils.

How to make the mask
Cut around the shape.
Draw a face to suit a Greek play.
Colour it in.
Cut holes for the eyes.
Cut holes for the string.
Thread the string through the holes and tie knots.

PRIMARY SPECIALS! *Ancient Greece*

Architecture

Background

The Parthenon is generally considered to be the most impressive of the Greek temples. Built on the Acropolis in Athens between 447 and 438 BC, it was made of marble and housed a range of sculptures, including an enormous statue of the goddess Athena, to whom the temple was dedicated. Rows of colonnades formed parallel lines that helped to create regularity and proportion.

Many buildings throughout history have been built in or influenced by this classical style. Those built in the nineteenth century such as civic centres, galleries, museums and some railway stations followed the design partly to create a sense of stability and tradition. The British Museum is an example, built in the style of a Greek temple. The present building was completed in 1847 in Great Russell Street, London to house a range of antiquities. However, numerous examples of neo-classical architecture remain in towns and cities across Britain.

Using the activity sheet

'Add some columns'

The resource, 'The British Museum', should be available and the children can select what type of columns they wish to add. Some may wish to give a name to their building such as 'museum', 'library' or 'town hall'.

Working with the resources

'The British Museum'

This resource and the following one allow the children to draw parallels between Greek architecture and buildings built in the neo-classical style, and enables the children to compare the Parthenon as it would have been with the British Museum. Introduce the terms 'column' and 'capital'. The Parthenon has Doric columns and capitals, the British Museum, Ionic.

'Townscape'

Once the children can broadly recognise classical buildings, they should be able to identify this style in the picture and so pick out such buildings from the modern townscape.

Useful questions

'The British Museum'

1 Do you think these buildings were built at the same time? Why?
2 In what way are they the same?
3 How are the columns different?
4 Look at the tops of the columns (the capitals). How are they different?
5 What other differences can you see? (You could explain to the children what each building is after the discussion.)

'Townscape'

1 What buildings can you see that look like Greek architecture?
2 How can you tell they are similar?
3 Can you see what the capitals are like?
4 What are these buildings used for? Are any buildings where you live similar? How are they different from the skyscraper in the picture?

The British Museum

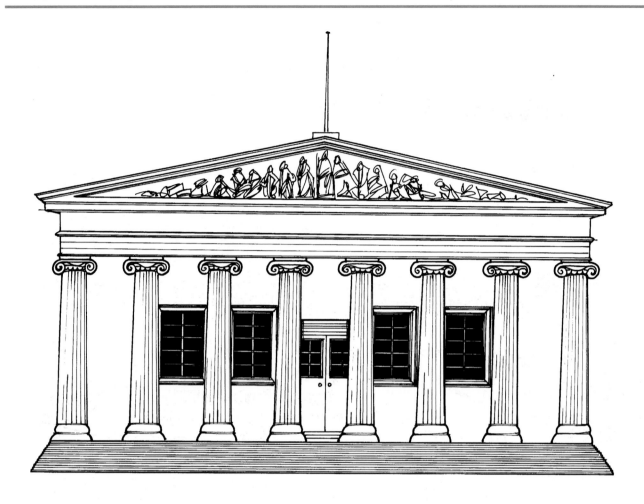

PRIMARY SPECIALS! *Ancient Greece*

Townscape

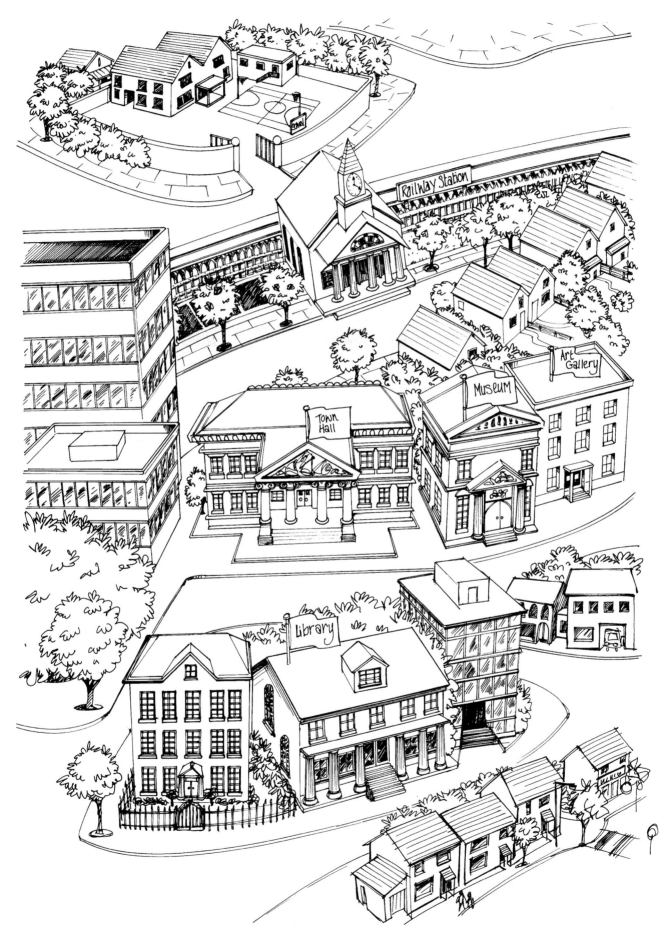

Add some columns

Finish the building by adding a row of columns.
Decide on the style of columns and capitals, then draw them.

The Olympic Games

Background

Evidence suggests that the first Olympic Games began around 776 BC. They were held on Mount Olympus in honour of Zeus and held every four years. They lasted for five days. All Greek citizens and youths could participate and existing conflicts between city-states were suspended. In practice, only the wealthy could afford to attend and the Games became increasingly important as a means to social and political power. They also meant access to greater wealth, since the winner conferred honour on his city-state, which would reward him handsomely. The modern Games began in 1896 and held to the Olympic ideal of promoting co-operation. A Frenchman, Baron de Courbetin (1863–1937), was largely responsible for their revival.

Using the activity sheets

'Similarities and differences'

Similarities between the Games are: *both stress the ideal of co-operation between countries, many of the same events take place such as the discus and the javelin, the Games are held every four years.*

Differences: *the modern Games open with celebrations while the Ancient Games opened with sacrifices, women as well as men can now take part, it is held at a different place each time, additional sports such as cycling and fencing take place.*

'Sports day'

The children can write a code of behaviour for their school sports day that echoes the Olympic code. Useful words are given to prompt ideas. They might also like to add a motto to their flag.

Working with the resource

'The modern Olympics'

Use the resource to compare the modern Games with the Ancient Greek ones. (See 'Similarities and differences' below, which you could complete during the discussion.) Discuss the ethos of co-operation behind the Games. The flag's interlocking circles represent the five world regions: Africa, the Americas, Asia, Europe and Oceania. The torch, however, originated in the 1936 Berlin Games under Hitler, in his effort to celebrate the Third Reich. Subsequently, it has come to mean 'unity'.

Useful questions

1 What kinds of sports are going on?
2 Are any the same as those of Ancient Greece?
3 Which sports are new?
4 Who is taking part? (Women as well as men.)
5 Do you know what the Olympic torch means?
6 Do you know what the flag means?

The modern Olympics

Similarities and differences

The modern Olympic Games are similar to the Games in Ancient Greece but there are also differences.
Write down as many of each as you can. The first has been done for you.

Similarities	Differences
Many of the same sports take place (discus, javelin).	*Women can take part in the modern Games.*

Sports day

1 Write down a code of behaviour for your sports day that is similar to the Olympic code.
The first line has been done for you.

Always respect the other competitors.

_____

_____

_____

_____

_____

Some useful words

sporting   **cheat**   **lose**   **boast**   **anger**   **brave**   **team**

2 Now design a flag for your sports day.

PRIMARY SPECIALS! *Ancient Greece*   © Folens (copiable page)

Having a Voice

This unit can be used in conjunction with the next one, 'Greek Democracy'. It gives the children the opportunity to make their own decisions after considering an issue.

Background

This unit presents the children with a dilemma: swimming baths have been suggested for Mill Lane in a local town, but land is limited and the baths can only be built where there is an existing adventure playground and play area for small children. Furthermore, the baths will have no paddling pool. By taking a vote when all points are aired and considered, you can explain to the children that what they are doing is participating in decision making. (You may wish to introduce the term 'democracy' if useful.) It is therefore best if the teacher works through the unit with the children, helping them with the activity sheets as well as the resource. This will free the children to focus on thinking about the issues and expressing their viewpoints.

Working with the resource

'Pool or playground?'
Initially, show the children the resource without explanation.

Useful questions

1 Look at the first picture. What are the children doing?
2 How old are they?
3 What animals can you see?
4 Look at the second picture. What does it show?
5 What are the people doing?
6 How did they get there?

Explain to the children what the two illustrations represent and the dilemma involved. Follow this by introducing the first activity sheet.

Using the activity sheets

'What do you think?'

Here different opinions are given on the swimming pool and the playground. The children should try to decide whether the comments are for or against the swimming pool project. They are then asked to add two more points, one for and one against but you can also note more points as you wish. Further points might be: (For the project) *local schools could use the swimming pool as well as the public*. (Against the project) *there are no facilities for small children at the baths who will also lose their play area.*

'For or against?'
The second activity sheet can be used in conjunction with the first and filled in by you (or a child, if appropriate). Once complete, the children can take a vote to decide on the outcome of the project.

Pool or playground?

What do you think?

Read these people's comments.
Then add one comment for and one comment against in the empty speech bubbles.

The wildlife will go as well as the playground if the baths are built.

There are no baths in the town. The nearest is miles away.

There will be more cars in the area.

Adults can use the baths as well as children.

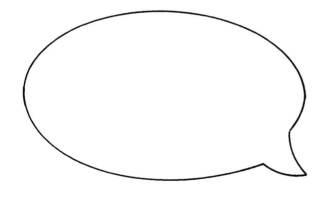

For or against?

List the reasons for and against the building of the swimming baths.

Mill Lane Swimming Baths

For the project	Against the project

Make a decision. Cast your vote!

Greek Democracy

This unit can be used in conjunction with the previous one, 'Having a Voice'.

Background

Government by democracy developed in Athens around 600 BC. It meant 'rule by the people', although in effect this was 'rule by the citizen', since women, children and slaves could not participate. A 'citizen' was a member of a city-state who could take part in passing laws at an assembly. It was workable because there were a limited number of citizens. Many city-states, however, were not democracies. Sparta, for example, was an oligarchy, which meant 'rule by the few'. Western democracies, which grew out of the Greek model, have their own structures. Britain is a representative democracy in which candidates stand for election and the candidate with the most votes wins. The main bodies are the executive (the Prime Minister and cabinet who create policies), the legislature (the Commons and Lords who pass laws) and the judiciary (the law courts who interpret the law).

Working with the resource

'In the market place'

Use the illustration to explain the meaning of certain keywords and expressions such as: 'citizen', 'freedom of speech', 'election' and 'vote'. You can also refer to the 'Background' opposite and the previous unit, 'Having a Voice'. Then outline very simply the right of British citizens to vote if they are above the age of 18 (with some exceptions, such as those who are certified under the Mental Health Act).

Useful questions

1 What is the person on the platform doing?
2 What are the people in the crowd doing? Why?
3 What are members of the crowd saying? What do they mean?
4 What type of person is in the crowd? (Males only; no women, children or slaves.) What does this tell you?

Using the activity sheets

'Citizens'

To complete this writing frame the children should understand the keyword 'citizen' and recognise who was not a citizen in Ancient Greece. Some children may be able to use the words 'vote' and 'rights' but others can still complete the frame without them. For example, in the second line they could write, '… should have a say in how the country is run' or '… should have the right to vote'.

'Running the country'

Here the children need to make the connections between the British democratic system and Ancient Greece (without necessarily using the word 'democracy') and also to recognise that no-one has the right to vote, including themselves, until they are 18 and even then there are some exceptions.

In the market place

PRIMARY SPECIALS! *Ancient Greece*

Citizens

Finish the writing frame about Ancient Greece.

We have been learning about how Ancient Greece was run. The Greeks believed that all citizens

A citizen was

But some people were not citizens, such as

This meant that these people

In my view the Greek system was

because

PRIMARY SPECIALS! *Ancient Greece*

Running the country

Finish the writing frame.

We have been learning about how Britain is run. It is like Ancient Greece because British citizens

To do this they must vote in

But not everyone has the right to vote. For example I

because

I agree/disagree with this because

PRIMARY SPECIALS! *Ancient Greece*